Grade 1 Writing

Y0-CDK-809

Contents

Print **a** and **A**.

Print the letter **a** under each thing that starts with the **a** sound.

Print **b** and **B**.

Colour the things that begin with the **b** sound.

Print **c** and **C**.

Circle the things that start with the **c** sound.

Print **d** and **D**.

Find these **d** words.

d	d	d	o	g
o	a	u	u	d
o	y	c	c	o
r	a	k	w	o
d	o	l	l	d

duck

dog

door

day

doll

do

3

Print **e** and **E**.

e e e

E E E

Unscramble the letters to spell words that begin with the letter **e**.

| sgeg | lfe | aet | eey | rae |

Print **f** and **F**.

f f f

F F F

Colour the things that begin with the **f** sound.

4

Printing, Letters, Sounds and Words

Print **g** and **G**.

g g g

G G G

Draw a line from the **g** in the middle to each thing that starts with the **g** sound. One is done for you.

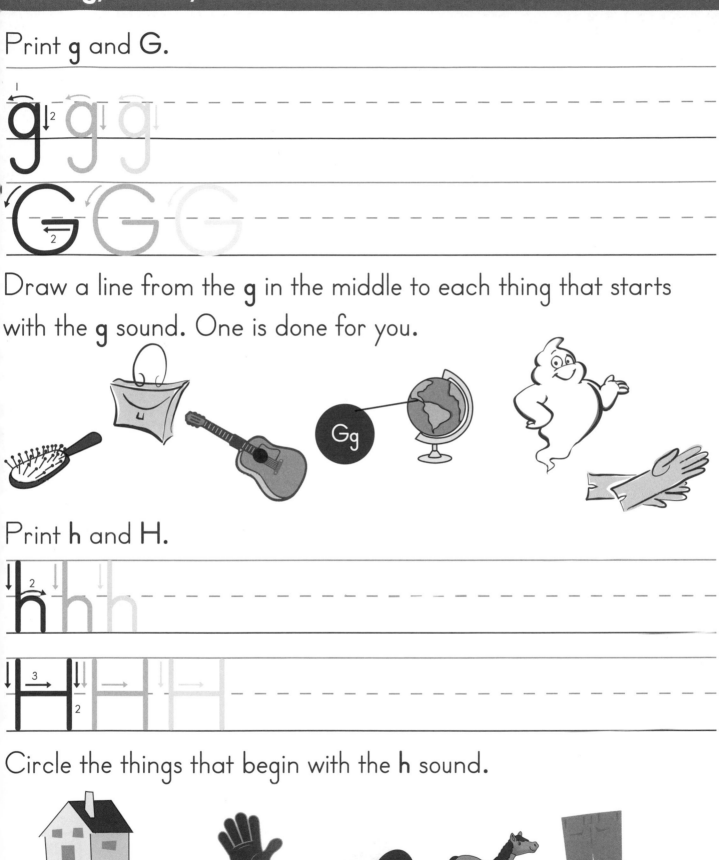

Print **h** and **H**.

h h h

H H H

Circle the things that begin with the **h** sound.

5

Print i and I.

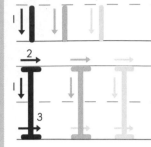

Print: Iris is interested in insects.

Print j and J.

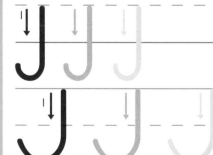

Circle the things that begin with the j sound.

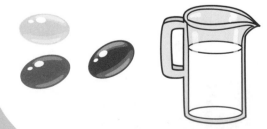   

Print **k** and **K**.

Draw a line from the **k** in the middle to each thing that starts with the **k** sound.

Print **l** and **L**.

Circle the things that begin with the **l** sound.

Print **m** and **M**.

Draw 3 things that start with the **m** sound.

Print **n** and **N**.

Unscramble the letters to spell words that start with the **n** sound.

| stne | lain | tsun | etn | enni |

Print **o** and O.

O O O O

O O O O

Print: Olivia opens oranges on her own.

Print **p** and P.

p p p p

P P P P

Colour the pictures that begin with the **p** sound.

Print q and Q.

q q q q

Q Q Q Q

Find these q words:

e	o	q	n	q	e	n	u
i	n	u	c	e	k	t	q
n	o	i	t	s	e	u	q
o	e	l	n	e	a	u	e
i	u	t	k	c	i	a	q
k	e	i	k	e	t	c	c
c	n	k	t	u	n	e	i
i	n	e	k	k	i	n	u

queen

quack

quilt

quiet

question

Print r and R.

r r r r

R R R R

Circle things that start with the r sound.

Print **s** and S.

S S S

S S S

Draw 3 things that start with the **s** sound.

Print **t** and T.

t t t

T T T

Colour things that start with the **t** sound.

Print u and U.

Print v and V.

Print w and W.

Print x and X.

Print y and y.

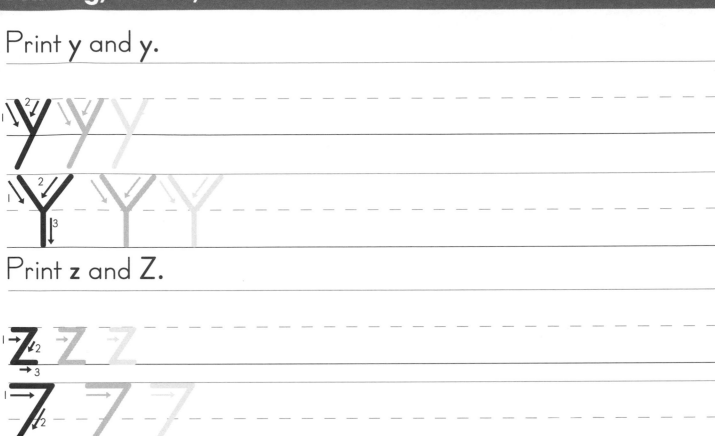

Print z and Z.

Find these **u, v, w, x, y,** and **z** words:

n	m	w	e	o	l	y	o	o
o	i	o	y	d	o	o	a	y
l	i	l	w	y	o	u	u	m
e	o	l	o	z	z	n	n	w
m	z	e	d	i	e	g	d	p
r	r	y	n	p	v	b	e	y
e	u	o	i	p	y	a	r	x
t	a	l	w	e	e	m	n	a
a	l	l	e	r	b	m	u	o
w	l	a	w	z	e	p	o	w

umbrella
watermelon
yoyo
van
zebra
xray
yam
violin
zipper
worm
under
yellow
zoo
window
young

13

Alphabet Fill in the Blanks

Print the missing **lowercase** letters in the peacock feathers.

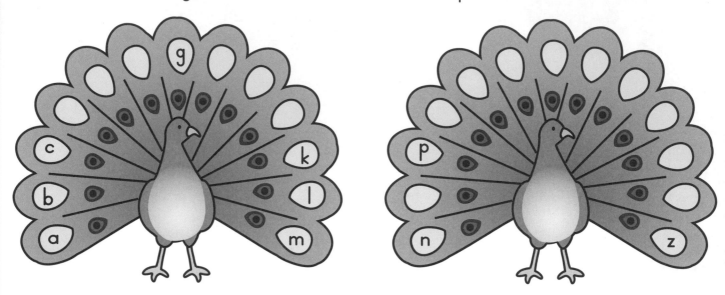

Print the missing **uppercase** letters on the beads.

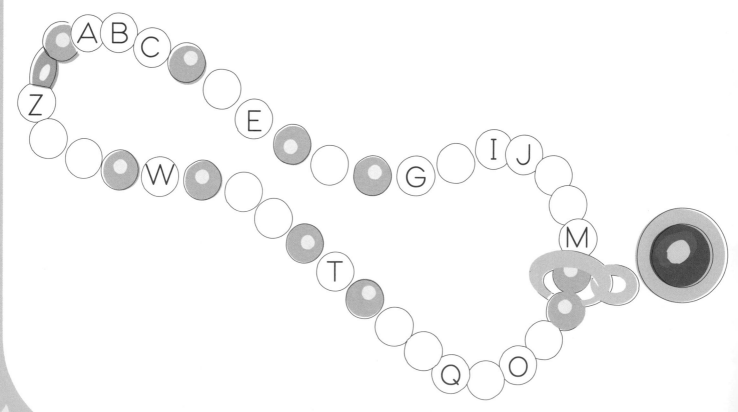

Days of the Week Trace and print.

Sunday

Monday

Tuesday

Wednesday

Thursday

Friday

Saturday

Colour each balloon to match the colour word.

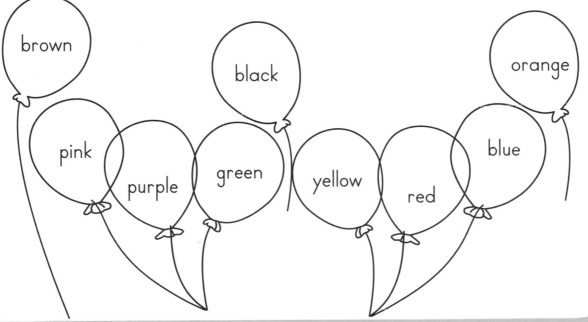

brown

black

orange

pink

purple

green

yellow

red

blue

Initial Sounds

Initial sounds come at the **beginning** of words.

Circle the letter that makes the beginning sound for each picture.

l f t	n h m	d c b	b f k
g h k	o a c	n r m	d c b

Draw a line from each letter to the picture that begins
with that sound.

p

s

b

l

m

f

g

Initial Sounds

Print the letter that makes the **beginning** sound for each picture.

Print the letter that makes the **beginning** sound for each picture.

_____un

_____hale

_____gg

_____iolin

_____am

_____ray

_____ebra

_____range

Final Sounds

Circle the **ending** sound for each picture.

t e h c	a g j y	g t c n	h d o b
o b p d	s r t a	d n k h	w v x i

Circle the pictures in each row that **end** with the given sound.

K

S

Blends

When 2 or more consonants go together they make a blend.
Say the name of each picture. Print the consonants that make
the beginning blend for each word.

fl   cl   gl   bl   dr   cr   tr   br   sp   str

_____	_____	_____
_____	_____	_____
_____	_____	_____
_____	_____	_____

Long Vowel Sounds

The letters a, e, i, o, and u are vowels.

Long vowel sounds say their own name.

For example: Long a is the sound in **snake**

Put an X on the pictures that have the same long vowel sound as the letter in that row.

Long Vowel Sounds a e i o u

Print the long vowel to complete the words.

b _____ at

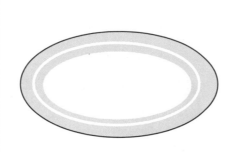

pl _____ te

_____ ce cream

p _____ e

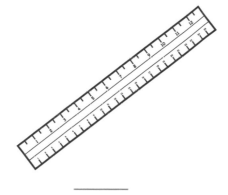

r _____ ler

l _____ af

p _____ as

f _____ ve

t _____ re

Short Vowel Sounds

Short vowel sounds are those you hear in **pat**, **pet**, **pit**, **pot**, and **putt**. Circle the pictures that have the same short vowel sound as the letter.

a

e

i

o

u

Add the Missing Short Vowel Sounds

Write the short vowel to complete the words.

c ___ p

p ___ n

fr ___ g

s ___ x

f ___ n

b ___ g

b ___ g

t ___ n

l ___ ck

23

It Takes Two — Compound Words

Two words can be put together to make a new word with its own meaning.

➡ Example:

rain +  bow = **rainbow**

snow + ball =

lip + stick =

pop + corn =

foot + ball =

Rhyme

Rhyming words are words that sound alike at the end of the word.

⇨ Example: **cat** and **hat**

Draw lines to match the pictures that rhyme.

Write the word that rhymes.

 hat

 bed

 toy

 chips

25

Antonyms

Antonyms are words that have **opposite meanings**.

Draw lines to match the words that are antonyms.

add	off
big	in
out	subtract
stop	go
on	small
night	day
float	sink

More Antonyms

Circle the word that is the opposite of the one on the left.

left	right
	up
up	top
	down
under	over
	near
cold	cool
	hot
bad	good
	red
sink	float
	drop

Telling Sentences

All sentences begin with a **capital letter**.
Telling **sentences** end with a period.

⇨ Example: The car is red.

Read each sentence.
Print it on the line using a capital and a period.

the bat is on the mat

my bike is nice

the fish is gold

my bed is big

Circle the correct sentence.

the frog is green

the frog is green.

The frog is green.

Asking Sentences

Asking **sentences** end with a question mark (?).

➡ Example: Is the pizza hot?

Read each asking sentence.
Print it on the line using a capital and a question mark.

➡ Example: will you play with me

Will you play with me?

is the helmet red

_____

_____

what is your name

_____

_____

Print the first words of each asking sentence on the line. Don't forget
to use a capital letter! End each asking sentence with a question mark.

➡ Example: ___Do___ you like cake _?_ (do)

_____ I have a cookie please ____ (may)

_____ many spoons do you need ____ (how)

_____ you sing ____ (will)

Sentences

Put the words in the correct order. Print the sentence on the line. Start with a capital letter. End with a period.

slow is snail a

_____

_____

music nice plays man the

_____

_____

swims the the in loon lake

_____

_____

map the check let's

_____

_____

skip to I love

_____

_____

Brainstorming Ideas

Write the words you think of when you see the following pictures.

Sorting Ideas

Draw a line from each thing to the box where it belongs.

moon

plane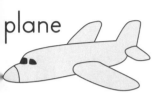

fish

helicopter

seagull

octopus

Things in the Sky

star

sun

cloud

Things in the Ocean

loon

submarine

lobster

Writing Sentences

Write a sentence to tell about each job.

 Veterinarian

_____

Astronaut

_____

 Zookeeper

_____

Chef

_____

 Pilot

_____

Writing Labels

Draw your bedroom and label the following parts:

door   window   closet   light

switch   lamp   desk   dresser

Writing a Description

If you could create a new kind of juice, what would it be?
Describe it. Then draw the label.

Writing a Story

Look at the picture. Write a story about it.

Write a friendly letter

Write a letter to a friend or relative thanking them for a gift.

_____

(Today's date)

_____

(greeting) Dear

Use a capital on the first word! Put a comma after the person's name.

_____

(body) Message you want to send.

_____

_____

_____

_____

_____

_____

(closing) Your friend, or Love,

Use a capital on the first word only. Put a comma at the end.

_____

(your name)

Writing a Story

Every story has a **beginning**, a **middle**, and an **end**.
Think of a fairytale you know. How does it begin? What happens in the middle?
How does it end? Write a sentence about each part. Put the title at the top.

_____

(title)

Beginning

Middle

End

Look at the picture. Write sentences about what you see.

➡ Example:
There are eggs
in the pan.

Procedural Writing

Write a sentence that tells what is happening in each picture.

First, _____

_____

_____

Second, _____

_____

_____

Then, _____

_____

_____

Finally, _____

_____

_____

Read the sentences. What comes first? Put numbers beside the other sentences to show the order they happen.

I go to school. _____

I get dressed. _____

I wake up. _____

I brush my teeth. _____

I eat breakfast. _____

First, **next**, and **last** are words that tell the order of what happened in a story. Finish each sentence to tell the order of what happened in the pictures.

First, _____

_____

Next, _____

_____

Last, _____

_____

Writing Activities

Writing Speech Bubbles

Speech bubbles in cartoons and comics tell what is being said.
Fill in the Speech bubbles.

53

Writing Lists

Lists keep us organized. Children like to make lists of their favourite songs, games, sports cards, or dolls. Make two lists.

_____'s Shopping List

_____'s Favourite Toys

Writing a Story Write a story about winter. First, think about it. Next, fill in the planner. Then write the story. Last draw a picture.

Characters: _____ _____
(no more than 2)

Setting: _____
(where does story happen)

Problem to be solved: _____
(by main characters)

Events:

1. _____

2. _____

Ending: _____

Use your ideas to write a story:

_____
_____
_____
_____
_____

Draw a picture here to go with your story.

Persuasive Writing

When you want to **persuade** someone to agree with your opinion or idea, you give reasons why your idea or opinion is a good one. Do you have an idea about something that you would really like to do? Now it is time to persuade your mom or dad using **persuasive writing**! Pick an idea below or think one up.

Ideas: get a pet   go to the park   buy some ice cream

Opinion: (e.g., I want to go to the zoo.)

_____

_____

_____

Two reasons or arguments to convince mom or dad that this is a good idea: (e.g., 1. I will get fresh air. 2. I want to learn about animals because I hope to be a vet when I grow up.)

1._____

_____

2._____

_____

Conclusion: (Rewrite opinion in different words. e.g., Going to the zoo will be fun and help me learn new things.)

_____

_____

Good luck!

Journal Writing

What is your favourite T.V. show? Write about it, including the title of the show, the names of the people in it, a funny scene, and what you like about it.

Days and Months Word Search

Find the days of the week and the months of the year in the word search. Print each one on a line below as you find it.

Days of the Week

_____

_____

_____

_____

_____

_____

```
Y W D A E Y A D S E U T E F
R R V D E C E M B E R C O D
U F E B R U A R Y R A Y R M
H R A A Y W E D N E S D A Y
M D D O Y R E B M E V O N F
O R T S U G U A J U L Y U B
R N M R E B M E T P E S E E
Y A D I R F Y A D S R U H T
E D S U Y A D N U S T U M A
J E A Y E N U J A N U A R Y
E Y S U E E Y A D R U T A S
Y A M O C T O B E R F J R Y
Y M A R C H M O N D A Y D H
Y T F A D Y A P R I L R R Y
```

Months of the Year

_____   _____

_____   _____

_____   _____

_____   _____

_____   _____

_____   _____

Solutions

Print a and A.

a a a
A A A

Print the letter a under each thing that starts with the a sound.

a   a   a

Print b and B.

b b b
B B B

Colour the things that begin with the b sound.

Page 2

Printing, Letters, Sounds and Words

Print c and C.

c c c
C C C

Circle the things that start with the c sound.

Print d and D.

d d d
D D D

Find these d words.

duck
dog
door
day
doll
do

Page 3

Printing, Letters, Sounds and Words

Print e and E.

e e e
E E E

Unscramble the letters to spell words that begin with the letter e.

sgeg   lfe   aet   eey   rae
eggs   elf   eat   eye   ear

Print F and F.

f f f
f f f

Colour the things that begin with the f sound.

Page 4

Printing, Letters, Sounds and Words

Print g and G.

g g g
G G G

Draw a line from the g in the middle to each thing that starts with the g sound. One is done for you.

Print h and H.

h h h
H H H

Circle the things that begin with the h sound.

Page 5

Printing, Letters, Sounds and Words

Print i and I.

i i i
I I I

Print: Iris is interested in insects.

Iris is interested in insects.

Print j and J.

j j j
J J J

Circle the things that begin with the j sound.

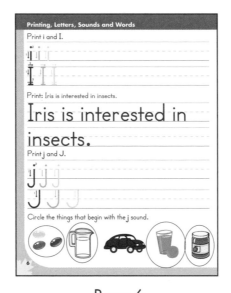

Page 6

Printing, Letters, Sounds and Words

Print k and K.

k k k
K K K

Draw a line from the k in the middle to each thing that starts with the k sound.

Kk

Print l and L.

l l l
L L L

Circle the things that begin with the l sound.

Page 7

Printing, Letters, Sounds and Words

Print m and M.

m m m
M M M

Draw 3 things that start with the m sound.

Print n and N.

n n n
N N N

Unscramble the letters to spell words that start with the n sound.

stne   lain   tsun   etn   enni
nest   nail   nuts   net   nine

Page 8

Printing, Letters, Sounds and Words

Print o and O.

o o o
O O O

Print: Olivia opens oranges on her own.

Olivia opens oranges on her own.

Print p and P.

p p p
P P P

Colour the pictures that begin with the p sound.

Page 9

Printing, Letters, Sounds and Words

Print q and Q.

q q q
Q Q Q

Find these q words:

queen
quack
quilt
quiet
question

Print r and R.

r r r
R R R

Circle things that start with the r sound.

Page 10

60

Solutions

Page 11

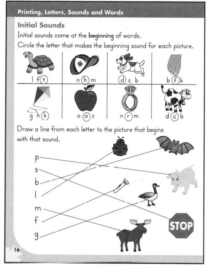

Page 13

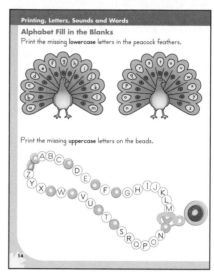

Page 14

Page 15

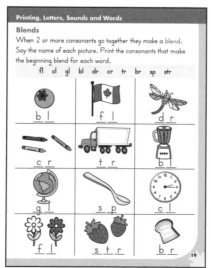

Page 16

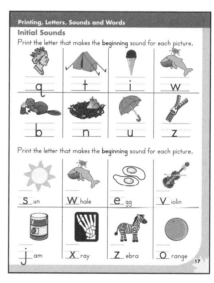

Page 17

Page 18

Page 19

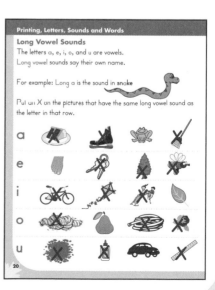

Page 20

Solutions

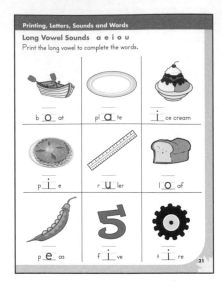

Page 21

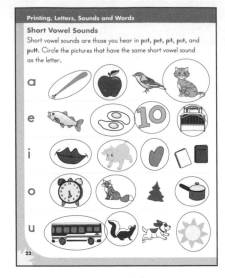

Page 22

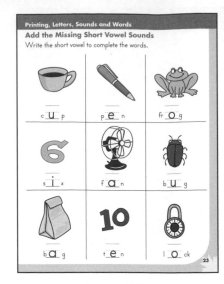

Page 23

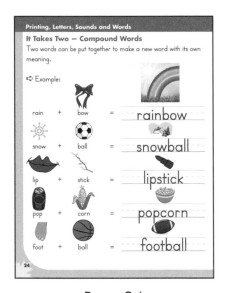

Page 24

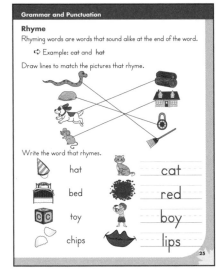

Page 25

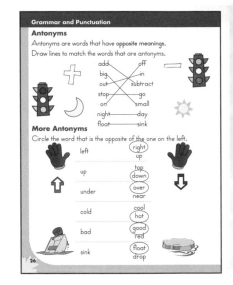

Page 26

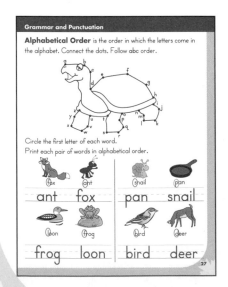

Page 27

Page 28

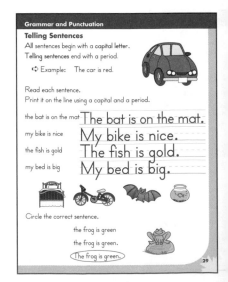

Page 29

Solutions

Page 30

Grammar and Punctuation

Asking Sentences

Asking sentences end with a question mark (?).

⮕ Example: Is the pizza hot?

Read each asking sentence.
Print it on the line using a capital and a question mark.

⮕ Example: will you play with me

Will you play with me?

is the helmet red
Is the helmet red?

what is your name
What is your name?

Print the first words of each asking sentence on the line. Don't forget to use a capital letter! End each asking sentence with a question mark.

⮕ Example: __Do__ you like cake _?_ (do)
__May__ I have a cookie please _?_ (may)
__How__ many spoons do you need _?_ (how)
__Will__ you sing _?_ (will)

Page 31

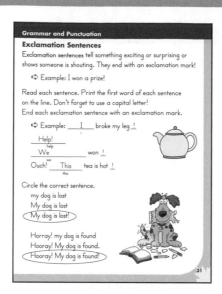

Grammar and Punctuation

Exclamation Sentences

Exclamation sentences tell something exciting or surprising or shows someone is shouting. They end with an exclamation mark!

⮕ Example: I won a prize!

Read each sentence. Print the first word of each sentence on the line. Don't forget to use a capital letter!
End each exclamation sentence with an exclamation mark.

⮕ Example: ___I___ broke my leg _!_

__Help!__
help
__We__ won _!_
we
Ouch! __This__ tea is hot _!_
this

Circle the correct sentence.
my dog is lost
My dog is lost
(My dog is lost!)

Horray! my dog is found
Hooray! My dog is found.
(Hooray! My dog is found!)

Page 32

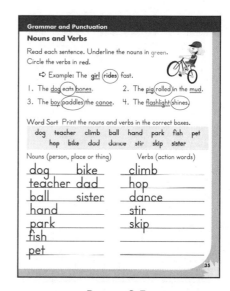

Grammar and Punctuation

Complete the final punctuation. Use . ? or !
1. How old are you _?_
2. I like to eat chocolate ice cream _._
3. My favourite food is pizza _._
4. What did you do on your vacation _?_
5. How fast did you run _?_
6. My dog can play catch with me _!_
7. I got an A on my last math test _!_
8. Does your teacher give you homework _?_
9. The weather today is sunny and bright _._
10. I want to have a fish for a pet _._
11. Who is your best friend _?_
12. My friend Mei Lei and I like to play soccer _._
13. We won first prize _!_

Imagine you went to a birthday party.
Make up 2 telling sentences about the party.

1. _____
2. _____

Page 33

Grammar and Punctuation

Nouns

Nouns are naming words for people, places or things.
Animals are nouns too!

Print the nouns in the correct box.

boy	yo-yo	mother	leaf
key	girl	book	park
iron	school	home	quilt
box	puck	vet	pal

Person	Place	Thing
boy	school	key
girl	home	iron
mother	park	box
vet		yo-yo
pal		puck
		book
		leaf
		quilt

Page 34

Grammar and Punctuation

Verbs

Verbs are action words that tell what someone or something does.

1. The kids __swim__ laps together.
2. The boy __jumps__ into the pool.
3. The woman __waves__ to the girl.
4. The boys __splash__ in the water.
5. The girl __reaches__ for her goggles.
6. A boy __sits__ on the side.

Page 35

Grammar and Punctuation

Nouns and Verbs

Read each sentence. Underline the nouns in green.
Circle the verbs in red.

⮕ Example: The girl (rides) fast.
1. The dog (eats) bones. 2. The pig (rolled) in the mud.
3. The boy (paddles) the canoe. 4. The flashlight (shines).

Word Sort Print the nouns and verbs in the correct boxes.

| dog | teacher | climb | ball | hand | park | fish | pet |
| hop | bike | dad | dance | stir | skip | sister | |

Nouns (person, place or thing)		Verbs (action words)
dog	bike	climb
teacher	dad	hop
ball	sister	dance
hand		stir
park		skip
fish		
pet		

Page 36

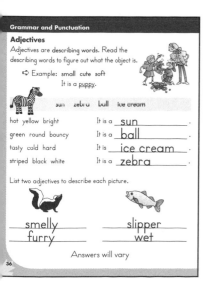

Grammar and Punctuation

Adjectives

Adjectives are describing words. Read the describing words to figure out what the object is.

⮕ Example: small cute soft
It is a puppy.

| sun | zebra | ball | ice cream |

hot yellow bright	It is a __sun__ .
green round bouncy	It is a __ball__ .
tasty cold hard	It is __ice cream__ .
striped black white	It is a __zebra__ .

List two adjectives to describe each picture.

__smelly__
__furry__

__slipper__
__wet__

Answers will vary

Page 37

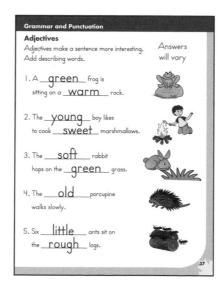

Grammar and Punctuation

Adjectives

Adjectives make a sentence more interesting.
Add describing words.

Answers will vary

1. A __green__ frog is sitting on a __warm__ rock.

2. The __young__ boy likes to cook __sweet__ marshmallows.

3. The __soft__ rabbit hops on the __green__ grass.

4. The __old__ porcupine walks slowly.

5. Six __little__ ants sit on the __rough__ logs.

Page 38

Grammar and Punctuation

Sentences

Read the sentence. Follow the directions.

X̲Ali̲ scored a (goal) today.

1. Underline the word "scored."
2. Circle the word that tells what Ali scored.
3. Put an X on the word that tells who scored a goal.
4. Put a box around when Ali scored a goal.
5. Draw a picture of Ali scoring a goal.

Solutions

Page 39

Sentences

Put the words in the correct order. Print the sentence on the line. Start with a capital letter. End with a period.

slow is snail a

A snail is slow.

music nice plays man the

The man plays nice music.

swims the the in loon lake

The loon swims in the lake.

map the check let's

Let's check the map.

skip to I love

I love to skip.

Page 39

Page 41

Sorting Ideas

Draw a line from each thing to the box where it belongs.

moon
plane
fish
helicopter
sun
cloud
submarine

seagull
octopus
star
loon
lobster

Things in the Sky

Things in the Ocean

Page 41

Page 51

Procedural Writing

Write a sentence that tells what is happening in each picture.

First, gather slices of bread, a tomato, lettuce and a cucumber.

Second, slice the vegetables and put them on one slice. Put butter on the second slice.

Then, put the second slice of bread on top of the vegetables.

Finally, cut the sandwich in half.

Page 51

Page 52

Read the sentences. What comes first? Put numbers beside the other sentences to show the order they happen.

I go to school.   5
I get dressed.   2
I wake up.   1
I brush my teeth.   4
I eat breakfast.   3

First, **next**, and **last** are words that tell the order of what happened in a story. Finish each sentence to tell the order of what happened in the pictures.

First, I planted a seed.

Next, I watered it.

Last, the flower grew.

Page 52

Page 59

Days and Months Word Search

Find the days of the week and the months of the year in the word search. Print each one on a line below as you find it.

Days of the Week

Monday
Tuesday
Wednesday
Thursday
Friday
Saturday
Sunday

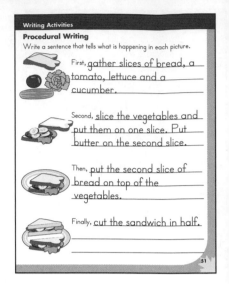

Months of the Year

January   July
February   August
March   September
April   October
May   November
June   December

Page 59